BRAHMS

Four Piano Pieces

Op. 119

Edited & annotated by

HOWARD FERGUSON

THE ASSOCIATED BOARD OF
THE ROYAL SCHOOLS OF MUSIC

Uniform with this edition

BRAHMS
edited by Howard Ferguson

Four Ballads, Op.10
Eight Piano Pieces, Op.76
Two Rhapsodies, Op.79
Seven Fantasies, Op.116
Three Intermezzos, Op.117
Six Piano Pieces, Op.118

CONTENTS

Four Piano Pieces, Op.119

INTRODUCTION

Johannes Brahms
(1833-1897)

The solo piano music of Brahms falls into three fairly distinct groups: (1) Three early, romantic Sonatas (C major, Op.1; F sharp minor, Op.2, which was actually the first; and F minor, Op.5), plus the isolated Scherzo in E flat minor, Op.4. (2) Five slightly later, self-disciplining sets of Variations. (3) Seven groups of shorter pieces that make up the present series of volumes, all being late except the *Four Ballads*, Op.10.

Besides these, pianists should not overlook the five splendid works for two players on one piano: *Variations on a theme by Schumann*, Op.23; 16 *Waltzes*, Op.39 (also published in two solo piano versions, simplified and difficult, made by Brahms himself); *Liebeslieder* and *Neue Liebeslieder Waltzes*, Op.52 & 65 (with four optional mixed voices); and 21 *Hungarian Dances*. And also, for two pianos, the *Sonata in F minor*, Op.34b, and *Variations on a theme by Haydn*, Op.56b, the composer's own versions of, respectively, the Piano Quintet in F minor and the well-known Haydn-Variations for orchestra.

SOURCES

Brahms took immense pains to secure accuracy in his published compositions. Furthermore, he kept a copy of the 1st edition of each work and noted in it any mistakes that had been overlooked at the proof stage. (Many works required no correction.) Hence it is these personally corrected copies rather than the autographs that provide the definitive texts of his music. He bequeathed them to the Gesellschaft der Musikfreunde in Vienna; and it is thanks to that Society that it has been possible to use them for the preparation of the present edition.

TEMPO

Brahms' main tempo marks are generally clear and unambiguous. But he used the word *sostenuto* in a special sense, implying a perceptible drop in speed. For example, in the Ballad in G minor, Op.118/3, b.71, *poco sosten.* is followed by *poco a poco in tempo* several bars later. Sometimes *sostenuto sempre* refers to a longer self-contained passage, as in the Rhapsody in B minor, Op.79/1, b.22. Here it undoubtedly remains in force for at least eight bars, and most probably for seventeen, since the vigorous mood of the opening does not return until b.39, where *in tempo* follows a further 2-bar *poco rit.* The duration of a shorter *sostenuto* is generally shown by dashes (*sost. – – –*), with *a tempo* implied (though not indicated) where the dashes cease, as in the Intermezzo in C, Op.119/3, b.10. But note that two

bars later the *sost.* applies to no more than a single quaver.

More rarely a similar drop in tempo is implied by the word *tranquillo*, as in the Capriccio in C sharp minor, Op.76/5, where *poco tranquillo* is shown at b.53, followed by *poco a poco più tranquillo* above bb.58-61, *rit. – –* above bb.65-68, and finally *Tempo I* at b.69.

Brahms never used metronome marks. When asked for the correct marking for his Rhapsody in B minor, Op.79/1, he replied that he could not give one, as it would be different for every week. And on several occasions he tried (unavailingly) to dissuade Clara Schumann from adding her own metronome marks to the posthumous edition of her husband's complete works.

In spite of this, the present editor has had the temerity to include in his Notes a suggested metronome mark for each piece. It must be understood, however, that it has no authority whatever, and may be ignored if the player so wishes. Far more important is it to remember that Brahms' music generally requires space in which to 'breathe', and will rarely sound right if forced into the straightjacket of a mechanical beat.

FINGERING

Though Brahms only occasionally indicated his own fingering – in these volumes it is always shown in italics – the shape of some of his broken-chord passages shows that they must be fingered in an unusual way. Instead of passing the thumb under the 3rd or 4th finger, or the 3rd or 4th finger over the thumb, the broken-chord is divided into complete handfuls, and the pedal used to mask the break in legato that occurs when jumping from thumb to 5th finger or *vice versa*. For example, in the Capriccio in D minor, Op.116/7, bb.61-63 must be fingered thus:

otherwise the effect of both slurs and accents will be lost. And in the Rhapsody in E flat, Op.119/4, the l.h. passage at bb.39-40 is undoubtedly meant to be fingered:

Many of Brahms' keyboard textures suggest that he had an unusually wide hand-span. Players not similarly blessed should discreetly break chords they cannot stretch, either as quick arpeggios or with the lowest note played as a gracenote before the beat and sustained by pedal.

ARPEGGIOS

An arpeggio sign (⸙) in Brahms often implies a momentary broadening of tempo. In theory the arpeggio should begin on the beat, and it generally does so when in the r.h. alone. If in the l.h. alone it often begins before the beat, its top note coinciding with the beat itself. The overriding consideration, however, must always be to avoid a thin tonal effect; so the player should interpet each arpeggio in the way that seems best suited to its musical context.

PEDALLING

The paired signs, 𝓟𝓮𝓭.   ❀ , indicate no more than the essential use of the sustaining pedal. Elsewhere, and often for a whole piece, Brahms expects the player to supply whatever pedalling may be required. Sometimes the general indication, *col* 𝓟𝓮𝓭., appears at the beginning of a piece, as in the Intermezzo in B flat minor, Op.117/2; but it may or may not be followed by anything further. In the same Intermezzo 𝓟𝓮𝓭.   ❀ does in fact appear twice in bb.8-9; yet it is interesting to note that the apparently similar passage at bb.21-22 is left unmarked, in spite of the fact that it needs different pedalling, with a change on beat 3 of the 1st bar (to match the shift in r.h. harmony) instead of on beat 1 of the 2nd bar, as bb.8-9 would suggest. In the Intermezzo in E flat, Op.117/1, the only two indications are *col* 𝓟𝓮𝓭. at the return of the opening (b.38), and 𝓟𝓮𝓭. in the penultimate bar; but this of course does not mean that there should be no pedal elsewhere.

Pedalled passages often contain rests and/or staccato marks (*e.g.* in Op.10/3, bb.3-6, and Op.10/2, b.91). Though illogical, this convention is acceptable because the presence of rests may simplify notation, while staccato marks suggest a type of touch or attack which, in conjunction with the pedal, produces a sound perceptibly different from that of a legato.

The sign for the 'soft' pedal, *una corda*, is rare; but it too may be supplemented by the player, so long as he doesn't get into the habit of adding it whenever he sees a *p*. Sometimes it is cancelled by the words *tre corde* or *tutte corde*, and sometimes the cancellation is left to the player's discretion, as in the Intermezzo in B flat already mentioned.

THIS EDITION

In the present edition numbered footnotes are concerned with textual matters and lettered footnotes with points of interpretation. Editorial accidentals, rests, dynamics, etc., are printed either in small type or within square brackets, and editorial slurs are crossed with a small vertical stroke. Curved brackets indicate that a note should not be struck. Brahms' fingering is shown in italics and the editor's in arabic numerals. Occasionally the editor has altered the distribution of notes on the stave, or employed the signs ⌈ and ⌊ (indicating respectively left hand and right hand), when this might make the text easier to read.

Warmest thanks are due to the Gesellschaft der Musikfreunde, Vienna, for providing microfilms of the 1st editions containing Brahms' corrections; to the Pendelbury Library, Cambridge, for allowing access to other 1st editions; and to both authorities for giving permission for the use of this material in preparing the present texts.

HOWARD FERGUSON
Cambridge 1985

EDITORIAL NOTES

The *Four Piano Pieces*, Op.119, and *Six Piano Pieces*, Op.118, were completed during Brahms' summer stay at Ischl in 1893. The two sets were published at the same time with the shared title *Clavierstücke*, Op.118 & Op.119; N. Simrock, Berlin 1893, Pl.Nos.10054 & 10055.

1   INTERMEZZO IN B MINOR

Adagio [♪ = c.63]

In a letter accompanying the autograph Brahms sent to Clara Schumann in May 1893, he wrote: 'It teems with discords. . . [and] is exceptionally melancholy. . . Every bar and every note must be played as though it were marked *ritardando*.' Though this was obviously a joking exaggeration, it nevertheless serves as a warning that the Intermezzo is no light-hearted trifle. It is, in fact, one of the most poignant short pieces that Brahms ever wrote.

Do not miss the expressive canon between r.h. and l.h. in bb.4-7 & 12-16. In the middle section, bb.22-23 & 35-38 should move towards the climaxes in, respectively, bb.24 & 39; and these are followed by a compensating slackening of tempo. Note that the chromatic inner parts that close the first half (bb.27-30) are carried over into the beginning of the second half by the tenor (bb.31-32) and bass (bb.33-34).

2   INTERMEZZO IN E MINOR
Andantino un poco agitato [♩ = c.82];
Andantino grazioso [♩ = c.92]

While it is obvious that bb.13*f*, 18*f* & 29*f* are different versions of the opening subject, it is less immediately apparent that the central *Andantino grazioso* is also based on bb.1-2.

The 2-note slurs in bb.1-2, etc., require that the first semiquaver of each pair should be lightly detached. As usual in Brahms, the *sostenuto* in bb.2, 8, etc., implies a slight holding-back, with *a tempo* on beat 1 of the following bar. It should probably be duplicated, though unmarked, in bb.6 & 10 (*cf.* bb.22 & 2 respectively). In bb.32-33 note the melodic inner part that begins with the rising tenor and continues with the falling alto.

The pedal-changes in the first half of the *Andantino grazioso* are on beats 1 & 3, but are more frequent in bb.52-59 where the harmony changes more often. The coda (b.101f) begins at the same tempo as b.36.

3   INTERMEZZO IN C
Grazioso e giocoso [♩. = c.88]

Grazioso e giocoso (graceful and playful) suggests that the mood is light-hearted rather than brilliant; so too quick a tempo should be avoided. The *sostenuto* in b.10 probably needs to be repeated in b.22; but the single-beat *sost.* of b.12 is *not* needed in b.24, where the harmony is moving forward towards a new key instead of curling back to C major. In b.62 the unmarked *a tempo* begins on the first of the r.h. semiquavers. Though the quavers in bb.65 & 69 require a touch of pedal to prevent them sounding dry, it should not impinge on the following rests.

4   RHAPSODY IN E FLAT
Allegro risoluto [♩ = c.112]
b.65 [♩ = c.92]; b.93 [♩ = c.80]

Suprisingly enough, the whole of section A (bb.1-60) is built of 5-bar phrases. The first change of pattern occurs in the 4-bar bridge-passage (bb.61-64) which both leads to, and anticipates, section B (bb.65-84). In order to make the connection clear it is helpful to stress the 3-note conjunct line that consists of upper CD in r.h. bb.61-62 followed by the lower E-flat in r.h. b.63. Likewise in the later 8-bar bridge-passage (bb.85-92), in which section C is foreshadowed by the rise-and -fall of the 5 notes: upper CD in r.h. b.89, lower FF-flat in r.h. b.90, and upper E-flat in l.h. b.91.

Resist the temptation to play bb.153-180 more quickly than the opening; and in bb.248-251 avoid collisions between the hands by following the editorial alternation of r.h. *sopra* and *sotto*.

FOUR PIANO PIECES
Op. 119

BRAHMS

INTERMEZZO

AB 1979

1) Bb. 34-5 & 38-9: the r.h. upper Ds are untied in both the 1st edition and the Complete Edition of 1927. However, a facsimile of the auto-graph Brahms sent to Clara Schumann (now in The Library of Congress, Washington) shows that he undoubtedly wrote the ties, but placed them so inexactly that they were mistaken for slurs by the copyist of the engraver's MS. Surprisingly enough, Brahms failed to correct the the mistakes in his own copy of the 1st edition.

INTERMEZZO

Andantino un poco agitato

AB 1979

Andantino grazioso

INTERMEZZO

Grazioso e giocoso

RHAPSODY

Allegro risoluto

(a) R.h. gracenotes before the beat. R.h. normal-sized notes coincide with the top note of the l.h. arpeggios.

Printed in England by Caligraving Limited Thetford Norfolk